TABLE OF CONTENTS

CONFLICTS OF THE GODS

The grim and glorious Aesir (AY-zir) were the gods of the ancient Norse people. From their heavenly realm of Asgard, they ruled over the world of mortals and the lands of the dead.

At the height of their power, the Norse gods had only one major enemy of note – the giants who lived in the land called Jötunheim (YOH-toon-heym). Ancient treaties kept outright war from breaking out, but no treaty could turn the gods and giants into friends.

However, the fragile peace was occasionally broken by conflicts between the two sides. These conflicts often involved Thor, the proudest and strongest of the Aesir's warriors. Armed with his magical war hammer, Mjölnir (MYOHL-neer), Thor is nearly unstoppable when his anger is aroused against his enemies.

Loki, a giant with a gift for trickery, is often found at Thor's side during his adventures. Time and again, the two blood brothers challenge giant troublemakers. For Thor, it's all about bringing justice and honour to the Aesir and to Asgard.

But for Loki, their adventures often provide opportunities to embarrass his brother...

FRIENDS AND FOES

 **Odin** – the one-eyed All-Father and wise ruler of the Norse gods. Odin is the god of many things, including healing, sorcery, battle and poetry.

 **Thor** – the red-headed, quick-tempered son of Odin. He is the Norse god of thunder, lightning and strength.

 **Loki** – a small giant and blood brother to the gods. A clever and magical shape-shifter, Loki enjoys tricking the Norse gods and humiliating Thor.

 **Thialfi** – a young servant to Thor. The mortal son of a simple farmer, Thialfi sometimes helps the Norse god during his adventures.

 **Geirröd** (GAY-rohd) – a nasty giant from the land of Jötunheim. Known as the Spear-Reddener, Geirröd hates the Aesir and longs to tear down the halls of Asgard once and for all.

 **Gjalp** and **Greip** (GEE-yalp and GRAYP) – Geirröd's twin daughters. Like their father, they live to see the people of Asgard humbled and killed.

 **Hrungnir** (HROONG-near) – a giant ambassador from the land of Jötunheim. He drinks too much and often offends those around him. His most fearsome weapon is the clay giant Mokkurkalfi that obeys his every command.

 **Thrym** – the dashing giant king of greater Jötunheim. He is a rogue and a thief. His mind is set on stealing the most precious treasure he can imagine – the heart of the lovely Freya, goddess of love and beauty.

CHAPTER 1
GODS AND GIANTS

In the days of old, Jötunheim was a land of bitter cold and shrieking wind.

It lay across the river Ifing.

Giants lived there.

Despite their size, the giants were not so different from us. Some were good, kind folk, just like we gods of Asgard.

But stories of good, kind folk do not interest me.

I am Odin, All-Father of the gods. In all my years, I have known many giants.

And many of them were cruel, wicked creatures. Those stories are my favourites.

But those tales do not belong to the giants alone.

They also belong to my sons, Thor and Loki.

Loki himself was a giant, though a rather small one.

I took him in as a baby to help create peace between Asgard and Jötunheim … between the gods and the giants.

Loki often gave me cause to regret raising him as one of my own.

Thor, on the other hand, was strong, brave and tough.

He taught the giants to fear Asgard. To fear us.

My sons are gone now. I miss them terribly.

But they will live forever in their stories…

CHAPTER 2
THE TALE OF GEIRRÖD AND HIS DAUGHTERS

One day, Loki borrowed a magical cloak of falcon feathers from the lovely goddess Freya. The cloak turned anyone who wore it into a falcon.

Alone, Loki flew to visit Jötunheim, the land of the giants.

But once he crossed the river Ifing, Loki was spotted. A wicked giant called Geirröd saw through his disguise.

That *falcon* is not a falcon at all.

With a pair of tongs, Geirröd hurled a burning coal at Loki.

FS-SZ-ZH

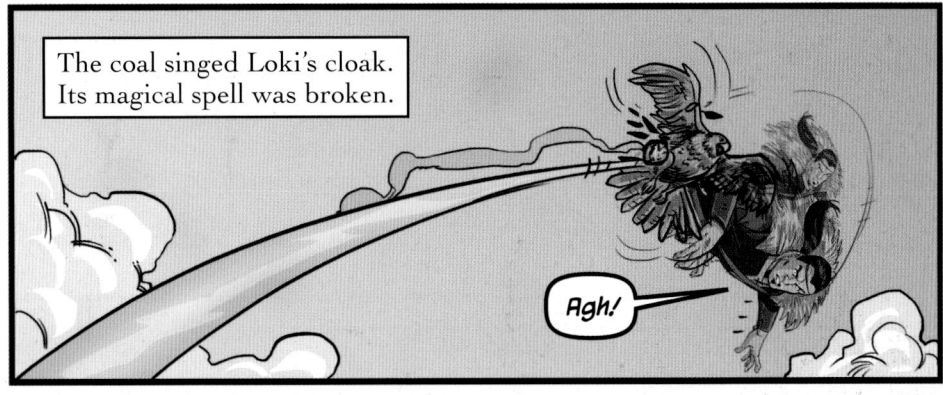

The coal singed Loki's cloak. Its magical spell was broken.

Agh!

Loki tumbled from the sky like a falling star.

WHUMP

When Loki landed, he found Geirröd and his daughters waiting.

You sly *traitor* to giants! Why have you come here?

Pin him to the earth like a *bug*, father!

No, let's lock him in a casket and bury him like the *worm* he is.

Perhaps we will do both.

Loki trembled at the threat. His bravery deserted him, but not his wit and cunning...

Wait! If you let me live, then I will give you Thor!

You would trade Thor's life for your own?

Yes. I can bring him here. Kill him, and the power of Asgard will be broken.

Very well. Bring him to me. But make sure he leaves his hammer, *Mjölnir*, at home.

Loki gave Geirröd his word. Then he returned home to Asgard.

Loki found Thor at his hall, Bilskirnir. In those days, Thor still trusted Loki.

Brother! I've just returned from *Jötunheim!*

I met two *beautiful* giant women named Gjalp and Greip. I told them all about you.

Go on...

They want to meet the mighty *Thor!* Are you interested?

Absolutely! We shall leave at once.

The brothers set out from Asgard in Thor's chariot.

They crossed Bifrost, the Rainbow Bridge, into Jötunheim.

At nightfall, Thor and Loki stopped to rest at the home of Grid.

Grid was a friendly giant. She welcomed them happily.

After dinner, while Loki slept, Thor told Grid why he was in Jötunheim.

I know Gjalp and Greip's father, Geirröd. He is a wicked giant.

He hates Asgard and all its gods. If you even *look* at his daughters, he will kill you.

And where is your hammer, Mjölnir?

My brother convinced me to leave it at home...

Hmm ... wait here.

Where are those ... *a-ha!* These should help.

This staff is magical. It is also *unbreakable*.

These gloves are as hard as iron and as *flexible* as leather.

Thank you, Grid. I'm certain these gifts will be useful.

The next morning, Thor and Loki set out once more.

Why didn't *I* get any gifts?

You snore.

Soon, they came to a river. The water was swift and cold.

They had to leave Thor's chariot behind.

These giant women had better be truly beautiful, Loki.

You won't believe your *eyes*, my brother. I promise.

The house was dark and empty with only a single stool for furniture.

Go on inside, brother.

Welcome, Thor... Sit, please...

Gjalp? Greip? Is that you? Don't be so shy!

Please sit down. We'll come out in a moment...

Ladies are so silly. Very well, I'll wait here.

As soon as Thor sat down ...

Gjalp and Greip emerged from their hiding place.

WOOSH

They grabbed the table and tried to crush Thor against the roof beams overhead.

Only Thor's quick thinking saved his skull from being caved in.

THUNK

That and Grid's magical staff, of course.

Then, with a mighty shove, Thor pushed himself – and the daughters – back to the floor.

CRASH

Outside, Loki assumed his treachery was complete ...

Sorry, brother. It was you or me.

... but Thor still lived. He had crushed Gjalp and Greip in their own trap.

Sorry, girls. It was you or me.

With his daughters' trap foiled, Geirröd took matters into his own hands.

You will *die* for this, Asgardian!

...IT WAS A TRAP FOR *THEM!*

You see, I knew you could handle them! That's why I took you to Grid's home first.

She gave you exactly what you needed to *survive*, remember?

Aye ... that she did.

Because you're my brother, I choose to believe you, Loki.

But next time, please tell me the plan first.

Of course.

And so the brothers returned to Asgard, leaving the house of Geirröd behind forever.

CHAPTER 3
THE TALE OF THE CLAY GIANT

Some giants became our enemies not out of wickedness, but from stupidity. Hrungnir was one such giant.

As the ruler of Asgard, I once invited him for a meal. He was a poor guest.

He drank too much during dinner. Then he insulted me – and my wife, Frigg.

This little old man doesn't **deserve** a queen like you. You should marry me!

I've had enough of this *oaf!* Thor, throw him out of Asgard!

Happily, All-Father!

The very next morning …

WHISPER WHISPER

… my raven told me Hrungnir was on his way back.

That foolish lout!

He carried a sturdy stone in one hand as a throwing weapon.

In his other hand, he held an unbreakable magic shield.

Mighty weapons indeed …

…but before him strode his true weapon — a monster made of clay.

Hrungnir had created it with his magic.

He called it Mokkurkalfi.

The colossal monster shook the land with each step.

I sent Thor and his servant, Thialfi, to deal with Hrungnir and his creation.

Thor wore his magical iron gloves. A belt of giant strength circled his waist.

And in his hand, he held his mighty hammer, Mjölnir.

Hrungnir's shield is going to make things difficult for you.

Aye.

I have a plan. You greet the clay giant. I will take care of its master.

Aye.

While Thor waited for Mokkurkalfi, Thialfi dodged around the clay monster to face Hrungnir.

At the walls of Asgard, Thor greeted the gigantic clay monster …

That's *far enough, monster!*

…with a single blow.

THOK

With Mokkurkalfi easily defeated, Thor set out for Hrungnir.

Thialfi found the giant first.

Thor has defeated your clay giant, Hrungnir.

If you don't turn back, you will be next.

Ha! Even Mjölnir is no match for my *shield*, boy!

Thor knows this very well. That's why he won't attack you head on.

Instead, he's digging through the earth to attack you from *below!*

Oh yeah? Well let's see him dig through that!

Hrungnir, as I mentioned, was quite stupid.

32

When Thor arrived, Hrungnir saw that he'd been tricked.

He hurled his stone weapon at Thor's head.

But Thor hurled Mjölnir at the same time.

CRACK

It shattered the stone in mid-air …

… and killed Hrungnir instantly.

THUD

What happened to the clay giant, Thor?

It should be here by now...

Aah!

BOOM

About time.

CHAPTER 4
THE TALE OF THE BRIDE OF THRYM

Elsewhere in Jötunheim lived a giant king named Thrym.

He was not hateful like Geirröd, nor stupid like Hrungnir.

No, Thrym was devious. Thrym was clever…

One night, he crept into Asgard in secret, right to Thor's home.

He stole Thor's magic hammer, Mjölnir, as Thor slept.

The next morning…

Robbery!

Brother, what is it?

Mjölnir is gone! *Stolen* in the night!

Loki first visited Freya in her hall, Sessrumnir, to ask for her help.

Why should I care?

Thor's hammer is Asgard's greatest weapon. He needs it back.

Without it, we're all at risk!

Fine. You can borrow my falcon cloak to look for it. It's over there.

Just be more *careful* with it this time.

Of course! You can trust me.

Loki soared over Asgard, following the thief's tracks.

The trail took him across the river Ifing, deep into the giants' land.

At last it led to the heart of Jötunheim: Thrym's castle.

Absolutely not!

Freya, please reconsider.

Loki, I'm *already* married.

So what?

SLAP

Well ... I tried.

Loki had no choice but to tell the rest of us what had happened.

We held a meeting in my own hall, Valaskjalf, to discuss it.

That is his demand. He'll only return the hammer if Freya marries him.

Otherwise, Mjölnir is lost to us.

I'll tear his castle down with my *bare hands* and take it back myself!

No! I forbid you from starting another war with the giants.

Freya, will you not consent to this? For the safety of Asgard?

Never! Thor may marry Thrym if he wants that hammer back so badly.

That's not a bad idea, actually...

May I suggest we *disguise* Thor as Freya?

That way, he can get close enough to the giant to get Mjölnir back.

I like no part of this plan except the end.

Oh, come now, brother. I would do the same for you.

No you wouldn't.

After much arguing and excuse making...

It's for the good of Asgard, after all.

Fine! Let's just get this over with.

Loki and Freya dressed Thor in a bridal gown and hid his face behind a veil.

I look *ridiculous.*

What does it matter how you look? It's what inside that counts.

Grrr...

We're ready, All-Father. What do you think?

Grrr...

I couldn't be happier. After all, every father dreams of the day his *daughter* goes off to be wed!

When the disguise was complete, we sent them off to Jötunheim.

They took Freya's chariot over the Rainbow Bridge, Bifrost.

Grrr...

Their journey was long but uneventful. Eventually, they arrived at Thrym's castle.

Finally.

They found all of Thrym's family gathered there. He had prepared a great feast.

Thrym greeted his new guests with great excitement. He invited them to join the party.

Thor and Loki took their seats at the giant's table.

Somehow, no one could tell that Thor was not the real Freya.

As Thor ate, however, Thrym grew suspicious.

Your appetite is ... *impressive* for one so small.

OM NOM NOM

Lady Freya's journey was long, King Thrym, and she is excited to marry you.

Normally she's a light eater.

Convinced by Loki's lies, Thrym leaned over to kiss his bride-to-be.

What he saw when he peeked under Thor's veil, however, gave him pause.

Does the Lady Freya have a *beard?!*

Not at all! Freya is just... *dirty* from the long trip. She will bathe before her veil is removed at your wedding.

And if I may be so blunt, my king, you've also had a lot to drink tonight...

Oh ... yes, perhaps you're right.

Thrym kept his hands (and lips) to himself after that.

When the meal was finished, and the kiss forgotten, Thrym stood up to address his guests.

Friends and family! We gather today not just for a feast – but for a wedding!

Today I make Asgard's loveliest ... *woman* ... my wife.

If you don't mind, your majesty, may I have Thor's hammer back now?

Of course. Someone bring Mjölnir to Loki so he may return it to Thor.

Upon seeing Mjölnir again ...

I have had *enough* of this!

Look upon me, giants! Mjölnir is *mine* — and mine alone!

That's Thor ...

... in a dress?

HA HA HA HA!

HA HA HA HA!

Consumed by his rage, Thor made the giants pay for their theft and mockery …

… there were no survivors.

When his fury was finally spent ...

So much for the supposed power of giants.

Loki, where are you? I didn't kill you by accident, did I?

I'm ... fine. How are you? Are you ... feeling better?

ABOUT THE RETELLING
AUTHOR AND ILLUSTRATOR

Carl Bowen is a father, husband and writer living in Lawrenceville, Georgia, USA, by way of Alexandria, Louisiana, and RAF Alconbury in Cambridgeshire, England.

His works include graphic novel retellings of classic sci-fi tales, original comics set in the world of freestyle BMX riding and high school football, and a far-out twist on the classic "Jack and the Beanstalk" story. He's also the author of the Firestormers series and the *Kirkus* star-reviewed Shadow Squadron series.

As of this writing, Carl has yet to try fighting giants with a magical war hammer.

Passionate comic book artist Eduardo Garcia works from his studio (Red Wolf Studio) in Mexico City with the help of his talented son Sebastian Iñaki. He has brought his talent, pencils and colours to varied projects for many titles and publishers such as Scooby-Doo (DC Comics), Spiderman Family (Marvel), Flash Gordon (Aberdeen) and Speed Racer (IDW).

GLOSSARY

Aesir name given to the collection of gods and goddesses found in the ancient Norse religion

appetite desire for food or drink

chariot light, two-wheeled cart

cunning intelligence; the ability to be sneaky or clever at tricking people

disguise way of covering or hiding one's true appearance; a costume

humiliate to make someone look or feel foolish or embarrassed

Jötunheim the land of the giants in ancient Norse mythology

mortal unable to live forever

tongs tool with two connected arms used for picking up things

treachery betrayal of trust through a deceptive action

veil piece of material worn by women as a covering for the head or face

weary very tired or exhausted

DISCUSSION QUESTIONS

1. In the first story, Loki tricks Thor into meeting with Geirröd's daughters so they could kill him. But Loki later says that it was really a trap set up to kill the giants. Whose side do you think Loki was really on? Why do you think so?

2. Thor easily defeated the boastful giant Hrungnir and the colossal clay giant Mokkurkalfi when they attacked Asgard. Why do you think Hrungnir believed he could defeat the Norse gods on his own?

3. When the giant king, Thrym, stole Thor's magical hammer, Loki created a plan to dress Thor up as a woman to get it back. Why do you think Loki enjoyed embarrassing Thor this way?

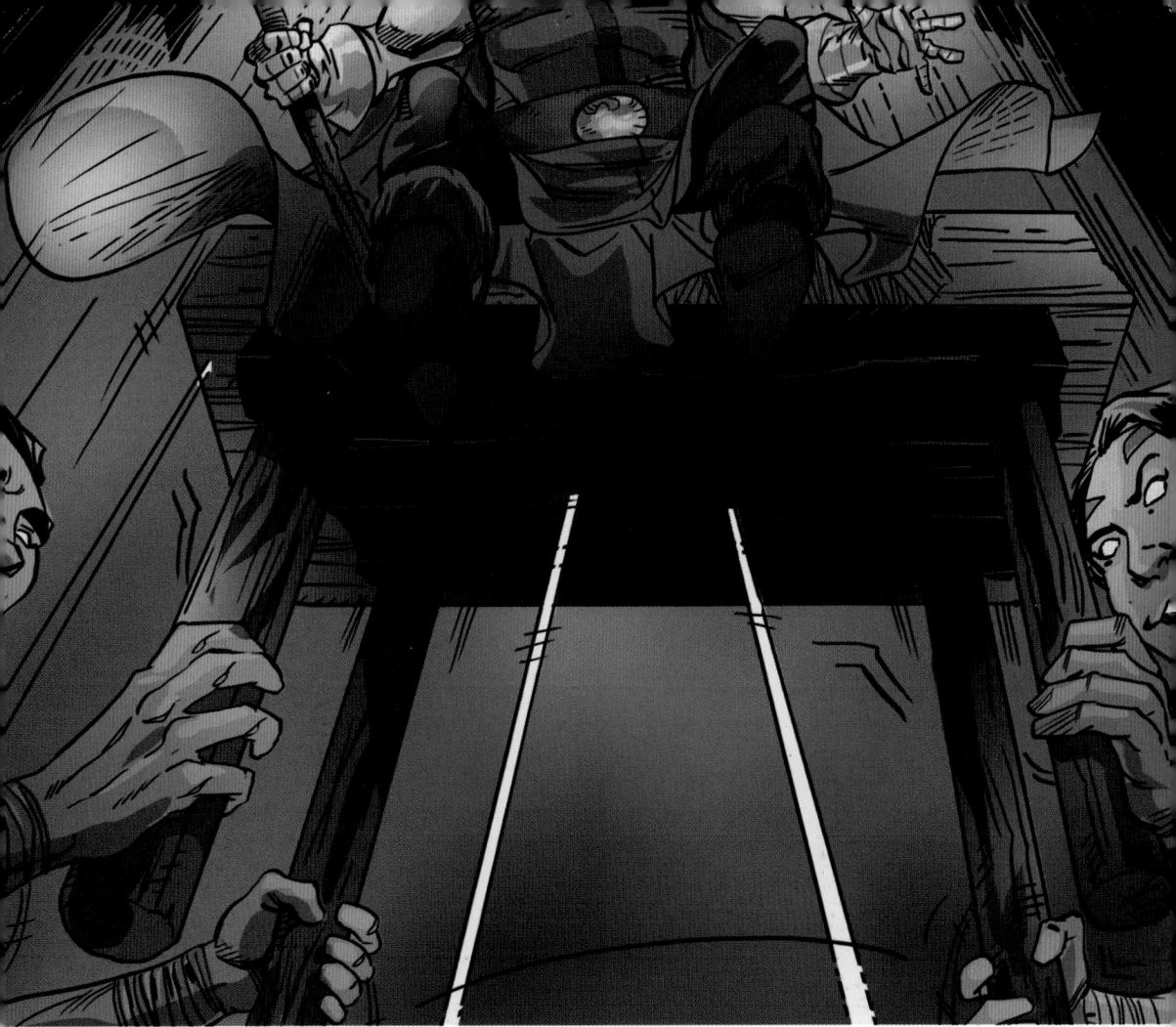

WRITING PROMPTS

1. After Thor faced Geirröd and his daughters, he was very angry with Loki. But he quickly forgave Loki for his tricks. If you were in Thor's place, how would you have reacted? Write down what you would have done differently.

2. Thor's servant, Thialfi, wasn't a god or a giant. He was a normal human boy. Yet he showed great courage by facing the giant Hrungnir by himself. Write about a time when you showed courage during a dangerous or scary situation.

3. After Thor's war hammer was stolen, could the Norse gods have tried any other plans to get it back? Create your own plan for how to recover the hammer, then write a new tale telling how Thor gets it back.

READ THEM ALL!

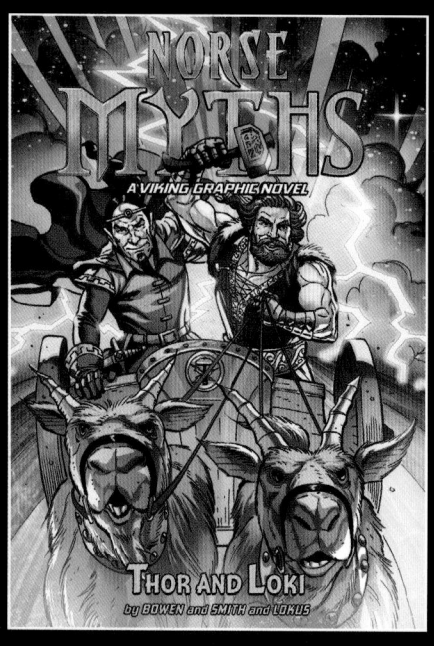

ONLY FROM RAINTREE!